# Reading STREET OKLAHOMA

## Program Authors

Peter Afflerbach

Camille Blachowicz

Candy Dawson Boyd

Wendy Cheyney

Connie Juel

Edward Kame'enui

Donald Leu

Jeanne Paratore

P. David Pearson

Sam Sebesta

Deborah Simmons

Sharon Vaughn

Susan Watts-Taffe

Karen Kring Wixson

**PEARSON**

Scott
Foresman

**Editorial Offices:** Glenview, Illinois • Parsippany, New Jersey • New York, New York
**Sales Offices:** Boston, Massachusetts • Duluth, Georgia • Glenview, Illinois
Coppell, Texas • Sacramento, California • Mesa, Arizona

*We dedicate Reading Street to*
*Peter Jovanovich.*

*His wisdom, courage,*
*and passion for education*
*are an inspiration to us all.*

**About the Cover Artist**
Daniel Moreton lives in New York City, where he uses his computer to create illustrations for books. He has two dogs—basset hounds named Zoey and Eddie. Can you find Eddie on the cover of this book?

OK ISBN-13: 978-0-328-33663-0
OK ISBN-10:     0-328-33663-7

2 3 4 5 6 7 8 9 10 V063 16 15 14 13 12 11 10 09 08

Dear Oklahoma Reader,

What interesting things have you learned in your travels down *Scott Foresman Reading Street?* What interesting people have you met along the way?

In this book you will read about treasures. What things do you treasure? We hope you will treasure the stories and articles that we have included in this book. They are about surprising treasures and treasures we share!

Have fun exploring the interesting information you will find on *Scott Foresman Reading Street!*

Sincerely,
The Authors

# Treasures

**What do we treasure?**

## Surprising Treasures

# Treasures to Share

# Treasures

**What do we treasure?**

9

# Let's Talk About
# Surprising Treasures

# Words to Read

| |
|---|
| give |
| surprise |
| would |
| enjoy |
| worry |
| about |

## Read the Words

Francisco wants to give his mother a surprise party. Francisco thinks she would enjoy it. But he does worry that she will find out about the party. Can he surprise her?

Mama's Birthday Present

**Genre: Realistic Fiction**
Realistic fiction is a made-up story that could really happen. Next you will read about a birthday surprise.

# Mama's Birthday Present

by Carmen Tafolla

illustrated by Gabriel Pacheco

What is Mama's
birthday present?

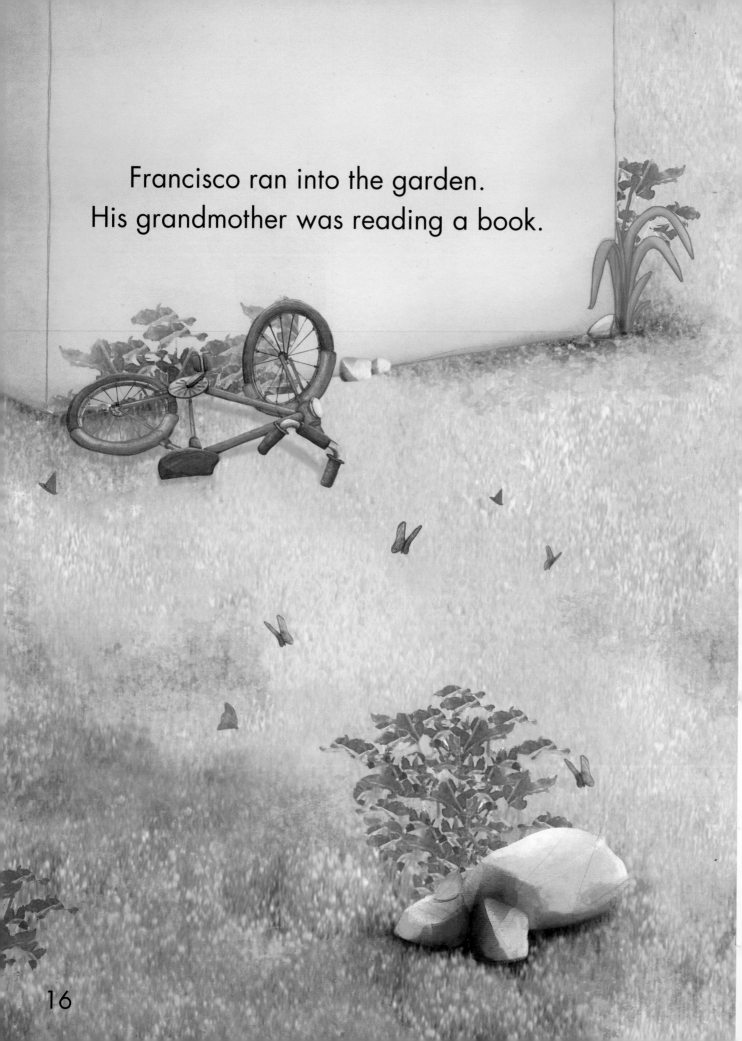

Francisco ran into the garden.
His grandmother was reading a book.

"Grandma! Grandma!" called Francisco.
"Next Sunday is Mama's birthday! Mama
always surprises me with a party for my
birthday. Can we surprise Mama with a party?"

17

"That is a wonderful idea, Francisco," said Grandma. "Today is Monday. If we begin today, we will have seven days to plan a party."

"Mama always gives me a present for my birthday," said Francisco. "What present can I give Mama?"

"I don't know," said Grandma. "But don't worry. We can make a piñata to break. Your mama will enjoy that."

So Grandma and Francisco made a piñata.

On Tuesday, Francisco wondered about
Mama's present. Francisco went to talk with
Papa about Mama's birthday party.

"What present can I give Mama?"
asked Francisco.

"I don't know," said Papa. "But don't worry. I can play my guitar. Your mama will enjoy that."

So Papa promised Francisco he would play his guitar.

On Wednesday, Francisco wondered about Mama's present. Francisco and his older brother went to invite Señora Molina to Mama's party. Señora Molina had a tortilla shop.

"What present can I give Mama?"
asked Francisco.

"I don't know," said Señora Molina. "But
don't worry. I can bring some hot tortillas,
fresh off the stove. Your mama will enjoy that."

So Señora Molina promised Francisco she
would bring hot tortillas, fresh off the stove.

On Thursday, Francisco wondered about
Mama's present. He went to talk to his friend
Gina about it.

"What present can I give Mama?"
asked Francisco.

"I don't know," said Gina. "But don't worry. We can make confetti eggs to crack on people's heads. Your mama will enjoy that."

So Gina and Francisco filled and painted the bright confetti eggs.

On Friday, Francisco wondered about
Mama's present. So he went to speak to
Grandpa Pérez.

"What present can I give Mama?"
asked Francisco.

"I don't know," said Grandpa Pérez. "But don't worry. We can make some sweet buñuelos. Your mama will enjoy that."
So Francisco and Grandpa Pérez made some sweet buñuelos.

28

On Saturday, Francisco still wondered about his present for Mama. But Francisco had many things to do.

He helped his brothers
and sisters look for a place
to hang the piñata.

He talked to Papa
about the songs Papa
would play on his guitar.

He talked to Señora Molina
about the tortillas she would bring.

He found a
safe place to hide
Gina's confetti eggs

and Grandpa Pérez's
sweet buñuelos.

Everyone was ready for Mama's surprise.

On Sunday, everyone came to the party.
Mama was very surprised.

Papa played his guitar. Señora Molina's
hot tortillas smelled wonderful. Grandpa's
sweet buñuelos tasted wonderful.

Everyone ate and sang and had fun. The children cracked confetti eggs over everyone's heads. Then they all lined up to take a swing at the piñata.

Everyone looked happy. Everyone
except Francisco.

"Francisco, what is the matter?"
asked Mama.

"I did not know what to give you for your
birthday, Mama."

"Oh, Francisco," said Mama. "This party was the best present you could give me. No, the second best."

"Second best?" asked Francisco.

"Yes. The best present of all is having my family and friends here with me. That is the most wonderful part of a party!"

Mama gave Francisco a big hug. Then they all took turns hitting the piñata. The one who broke it was Francisco.
And Mama enjoyed that.

# Think and Share

**Talk About It** "Don't worry," everyone says to Francisco. What advice would you have given him about what to give Mama?

**1.** Use the pictures below to retell the story.
Retell

**2.** Why was a gift for Mama so important to Francisco? **Draw Conclusions**

**3.** Did you stumble on any words in the story? What did you do about it? **Fix Up**

**Look Back and Write** What did everyone do at the party? Look back at pages 32–33. Make a list.

## Meet the Author

# Carmen Tafolla

Carmen Tafolla grew up in San Antonio, Texas. She tells stories and writes poems about her Mexican American neighborhood.

Dr. Tafolla works with schools around the world to help children of all races and languages to succeed. She lives in a 100-year-old house in San Antonio with her husband, son, mother, and lots of books.

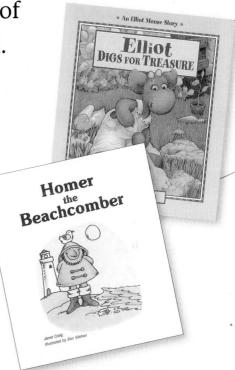

**Read more books about treasures.**

# Chinese Surprises

by Annie Brannan

Do you ever eat Chinese food? If so, then you may know about these Chinese desserts. Inside each one is a small note. The note's message sometimes gives advice.

If you take time to laugh, you would enjoy life more.

Don't worry. Work hard and good things will happen.

Sometimes a note tells about something that could happen to you.

Some day soon you will take a long trip.

Good things come to those who wait.

Why do people like these little desserts so much? People enjoy surprises!

## Book Review

### Prompt

*Mama's Birthday Present* is a book for children.

Think about a book you like.

Now write a book review telling why you like the book.

**Writing Trait**

All **sentences** in a book review tell about the book.

**Student Model**

**Book is named in title.**

<u>The Cat in the Hat</u>

This is a good book.

**All <u>sentences</u> tell about book.**

A strange cat visits two children. He makes a big mess. I like this book because it is funny. Everyone should read it.

**Writer gives opinion of book.**

42

# Grammar

## Adjectives

An **adjective** tells about a person, place, animal, or thing.

> The **tall** man pats the **cute** puppy.
> I saw a **red** rug at the **new** store.

- - - - - - - - - - - - - - - - - - - - -

Look at the book review. Write the adjective that tells about the cat. Write the adjective that tells about the mess.

# Let's Talk About Surprising Treasures

# Words to Read

| |
|:-:|
| **draw** |
| **colors** |
| **over** |
| **drew** |
| **great** |
| **sign** |
| **show** |

## Read the Words

In art class we draw with pencils. Then we mix colors and paint over the drawings. I drew a great big cat. Let me sign it. Then I will show it to you.

The Dot

**Genre: Realistic Fiction**
Realistic fiction stories are made up, but they have characters that seem real. In the next story you will see what happens to one small dot.

47

# The Dot

by Peter H. Reynolds

How can a dot be a treasure?

Art class was over, but Vashti sat glued
to her chair. Her paper was empty.

Vashti's teacher leaned over the blank paper.
"Ah! A polar bear in a snowstorm," she said.
"Very funny!" said Vashti. "I just CAN'T draw!"

Her teacher smiled. "Just
make a mark and see where it
takes you."

Vashti grabbed a marker and gave the
paper a good, strong jab. "There!"

Her teacher picked up the
paper and studied it carefully.
"Hmmmmm."

She pushed the paper
toward Vashti and quietly
said, "Now sign it."

Vashti thought for a moment.
"Well, maybe I can't draw, but I
CAN sign my name."

The next week, when Vashti walked into art class, she was surprised to see what was hanging above her teacher's desk.

It was the little dot she had drawn—HER DOT! All framed in swirly gold!

"Hmmph! I can make a
better dot than THAT!"

She opened her never-before-used
set of watercolors and set to work.
Vashti painted and painted.

A red dot.
A purple dot.
A yellow dot.
A blue dot.

The blue mixed with the yellow. She
discovered that she could make a GREEN dot.

Vashti kept experimenting.
Lots of little dots in many colors.

"If I can make little dots, I can make BIG dots too." Vashti splashed her colors with a bigger brush on bigger paper to make bigger dots.

Vashti even made a dot
by NOT painting a dot.

At the school art show a few weeks later,
Vashti's *many dots* made quite a splash.

Vashti noticed a little boy
gazing up at her.
"You're a really great artist.
I wish I could draw," he said.

"I bet you can," said Vashti.
"ME? No, not me. I can't draw
a straight line with a ruler."

Vashti smiled. She handed the boy a blank sheet of paper. "Show me."

The boy's pencil shook as he drew his line.

Vashti stared at the boy's squiggle.
And then she said . . .

"Sign it."

# Think and Share

**Talk About It** Vashti didn't think she could draw. How did her teacher help her? Has anything like this happened to you? Explain.

**1.** Which picture below is out of order? Where should it be? Use the pictures to retell the story.  **Retell**

**2.** What is the big idea of *The Dot*? What lesson did you learn?  **Theme**

**3.** Make a story map of *The Dot*.
**Graphic Organizers**

**Look Back and Write** Look back at page 60. How does Vashti make a dot by not painting a dot?

## Meet the Author and Illustrator
# Peter H. Reynolds

Peter Reynolds says *The Dot* "is a book that encourages us to be brave about expressing ourselves. It gently reminds us to start small and explore the idea."

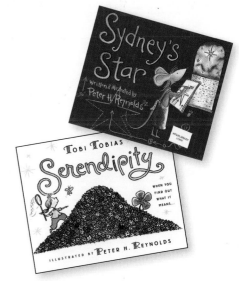

Mr. Reynolds collects ideas for stories in his journal. He likes to doodle on scraps of paper. He collects these little drawings in old tin boxes.

**Read more books by Peter H. Reynolds.**

# A Great Artist and His Dots

by Karen Stockwell

Georges Seurat liked to draw in the park.

He drew people and animals.

He painted lots of dots over his drawings.

The dots were many colors.

One huge painting he signed shows
ladies and men in a park.
Now this beautiful painting is in a museum.
People come to see it each day.

## Steps

### Prompt

*The Dot* tells how Vashti draws a picture. Think about how you draw something. Now write steps that tell how to draw it.

**Writing Trait**

Put your steps in the **order** you do them.

**Student Model**

Title tells what steps are for.

Writer begins with what is needed.

Steps are in the right <u>order</u>.

<u>How to Draw a Face</u>

1. Get a sheet of white paper and a marker.
2. Draw a circle with two round eyes, a nose, and a mouth in it.
3. Add lines on top for hair.

**Writer's Checklist**

- ☑ **Focus** Do all sentences tell how to draw something?
- ☑ **Organization** Are steps in the right order?
- ☑ **Support** Do the words make each step clear?
- ☑ **Conventions** Does every sentence begin with a capital letter and end with a period?

# Grammar

## Adjectives for Colors and Shapes

Some **adjectives** name colors.
Some **adjectives** name shapes.

Vashti draws a **blue** flower
and a **square** box.

· · · · · · · · · · · · · · · · · · · · · · · · · · · · · · ·

Look at the steps. Find one adjective
that names a color and one adjective that
names a shape. Write the adjectives.

# Let's Talk About
# Surprising
# Treasures

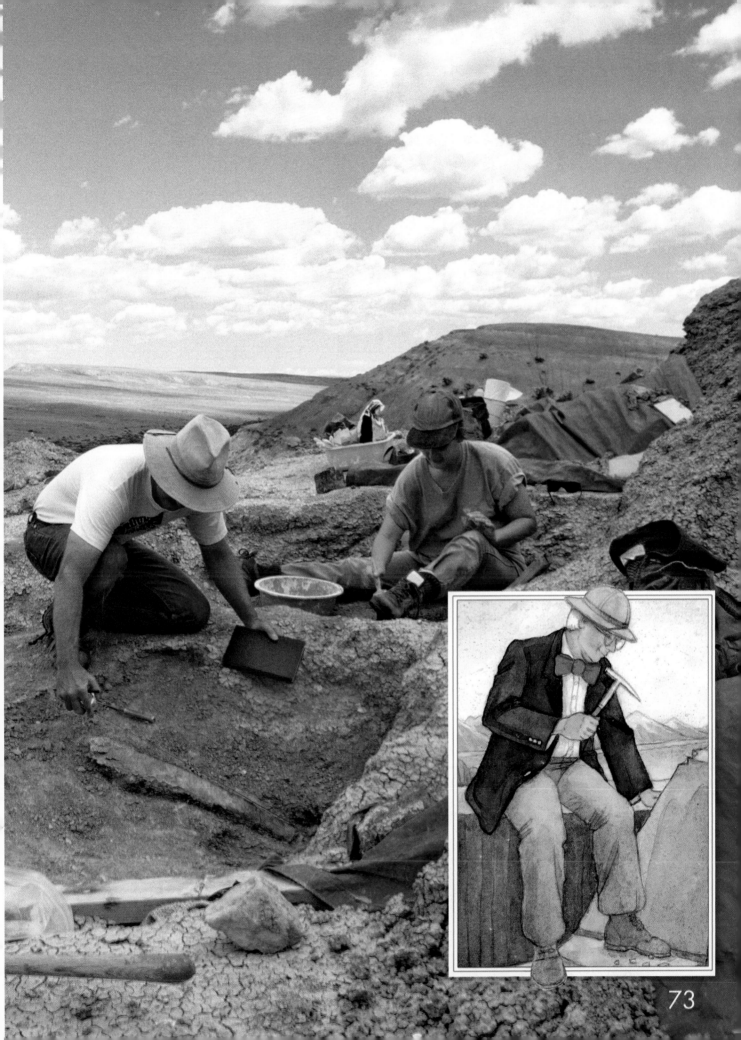

# Words to Read

| |
|---|
| once |
| wild |
| found |
| took |
| mouth |

# Read the Words

Once the wild T. Rex roamed the West. But not any more. T. Rex bones have been found in many places. Workers took the bones and put them together. Look at that mouth! Those teeth are sharp.

Mister Bones

### Genre: Biography
A biography is the story of a real person's life. Next you will read about Barnum Brown, an interesting man.

# Mister Bones

## Dinosaur Hunter

by Jane Kurtz

illustrated by Mary Haverfield

What can animal bones tell us?

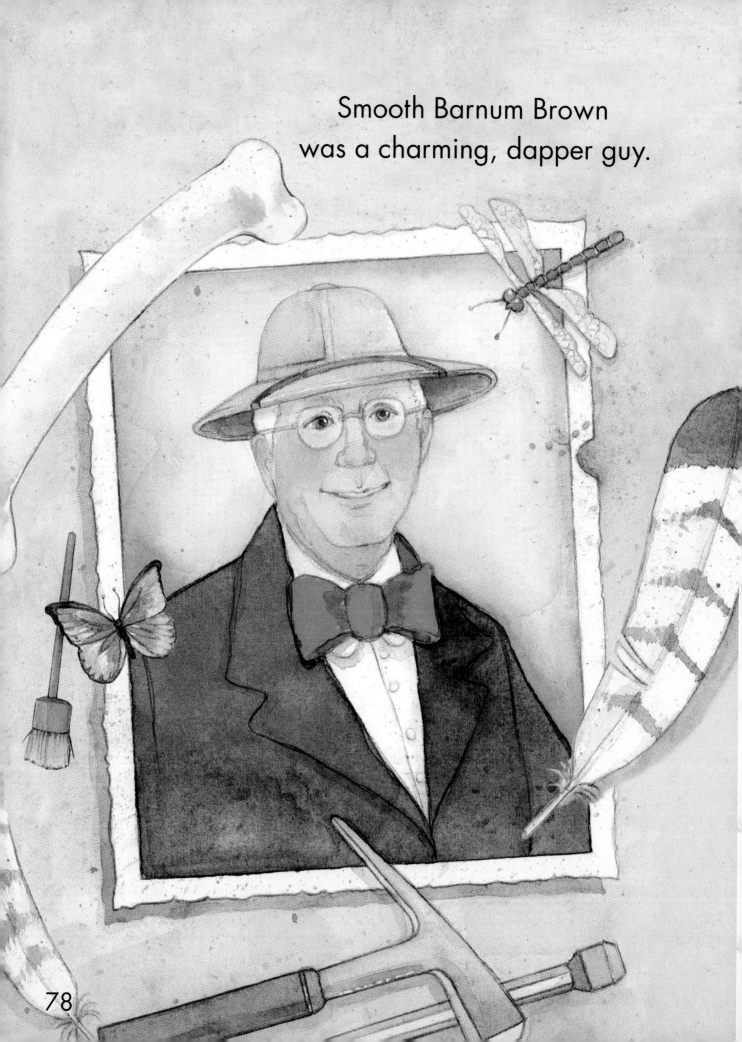

Smooth Barnum Brown
was a charming, dapper guy.

78

He went climbing over rocks
in a topcoat and a tie.

He loved ballroom dancing, but he was not dancing now. He was digging in the dirt. What was he looking for? It was not shining silver. His wife once called it rainbows, but it was not in the sky.

Others wore bandannas and cowboy boots and chaps. Mister Brown came to Montana in a fancy coat and hat.

He poked and he sifted and he picked in the dirt. Was he hunting gold? No, nothing quite that old.

But what he hunted, people wanted just
about as much as gold. Bones. Big old bones.

People said, "Barnum Brown can somehow smell bones." His nickname became Mister Bones.

Mister Bones found bones in the middle of Montana—a backbone and a hip bone and other bones and chips.

Bones were packed in boxes, shipped off to New York. Putting them together took lots and lots of work.

Step back! Imagine that! Now what about
a name? A name? Yes, a name for this
amazing thing.

That job went to the museum president.
Henry Osborn called it tyrant lizard king.

It was as tall as three men but had short, short arms. It had a wide, wild mouth and six-inch teeth.

Huge Tyrannosaurus. Gigantic T. Rex. Mister Bones had found the tyrant lizard king.

# Think and Share

**Talk About It** Old bones were treasures to Barnum Brown. What is a treasure to you?

**1.** Use the pictures to summarize what you learned about Barnum Brown. **Retell**

**2.** Why do you think Jane Kurtz wrote *Mister Bones: Dinosaur Hunter?* Author's Purpose

**3.** Henry Osborn called T. Rex a "tyrant lizard king." What is a tyrant? Use your glossary to find out. **Monitor/Fix Up**

**TEST PRACTICE**

**Look Back and Write** Look back at page 84. Could Barnum Brown really "smell bones"? What does the author mean?

# Jane Kurtz

Jane Kurtz has liked dinosaurs ever since her parents took her to Dinosaur National Monument when she was seven years old.

Ms. Kurtz did a lot of research for *Mister Bones.* "I had to learn lots and lots about Barnum Brown to find the most interesting facts to include. The research took months. The writing took only weeks."

**Read more books by Jane Kurtz.**

# What's in a

by Mary Rowan

Museums are great places. At this museum, you can find out about art. You can mix colors. Once you have the colors you want, you can be an artist! Splash it on!

# Museum ?

Where do the bones of a T. Rex go after they are found? They go to a museum! Workers took these bones and put them back together. Look at that mouth!

Some museums show you how things work. Look at this ball. Throw it up and watch it float. Why does it float? Experimenting with it helps you find out.

This museum shows where wild animals live. You can look in the windows and see their homes.

Visit a museum close to you. You can have loads of fun there!

# Write Now

**Writing and Grammar**

## Reasons

**Prompt**

*Mister Bones: Dinosaur Hunter* tells why T. Rex was special. Think about another dinosaur or another animal you know well. Now write reasons why that dinosaur or animal is special.

### Writing Trait

**Focus** is on why the animal is special.

### Student Model

First sentence <u>focuses</u> on main <u>idea</u>.

Adjectives describe T. Rex.

Sentences give details about T. Rex.

T. Rex was a large, scary dinosaur. It had a huge head and a big mouth. Sharp teeth and strong jaws made it dangerous. This special dino had long legs and feet with claws.

96

# Grammar

## Adjectives for Sizes

Some **adjectives** describe size. Words such as **big, small, long,** and **short** describe size.

T. Rex had **short** arms.

• • • • • • • • • • • • • • • • • • • • • • • • •

Look at the reasons why T. Rex is scary. Find four adjectives that describe size. Write the adjectives.

# Let's Talk About

# Treasures to Share

# Words to Read

| |
|---|
| **eight** |
| **moon** |
| **above** |
| **touch** |
| **laugh** |

# Read the Words

All eight of us looked at the moon above us. It looked close enough to touch. This night was going to be fun. We began to laugh.

**Genre: Realistic Fiction**

Realistic fiction stories are made-up stories, but they tell about events that seem real. Next you will read about a special celebration.

# The Lady in the Moon

by Lily Wong Fillmore
illustrated by Lin Wang

**Who is the Lady in the Moon?**

The sun sets. The moon rises.
Come out. Come out to play.
It is Moon Festival, a night
for children everywhere.

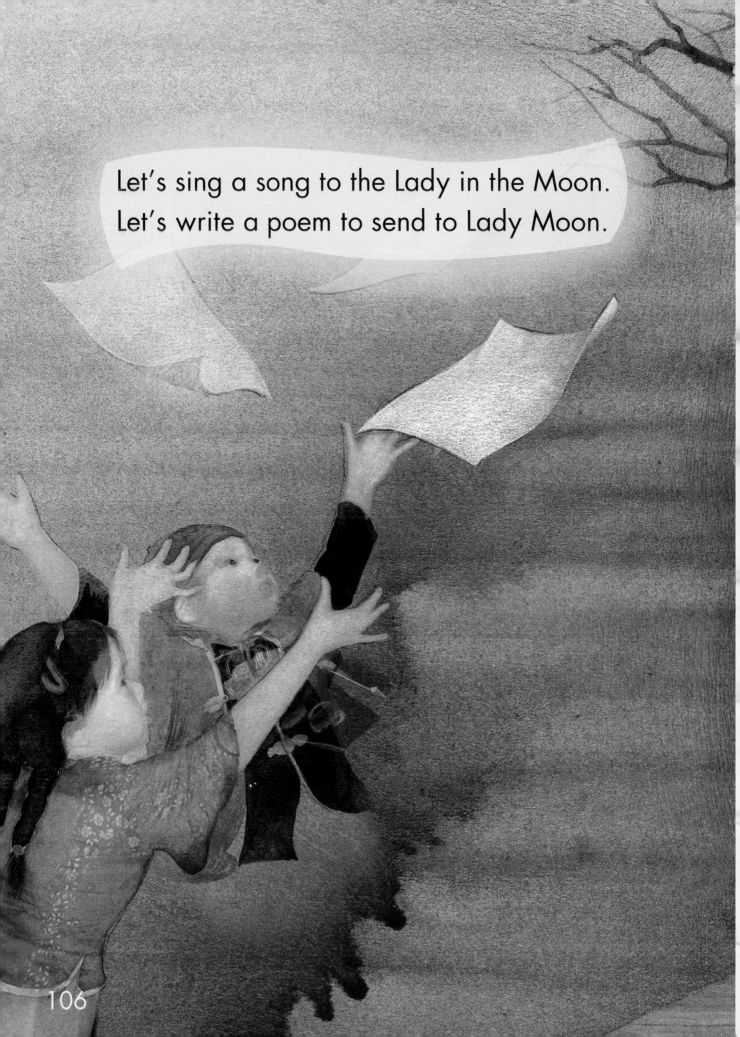

Let's sing a song to the Lady in the Moon.
Let's write a poem to send to Lady Moon.

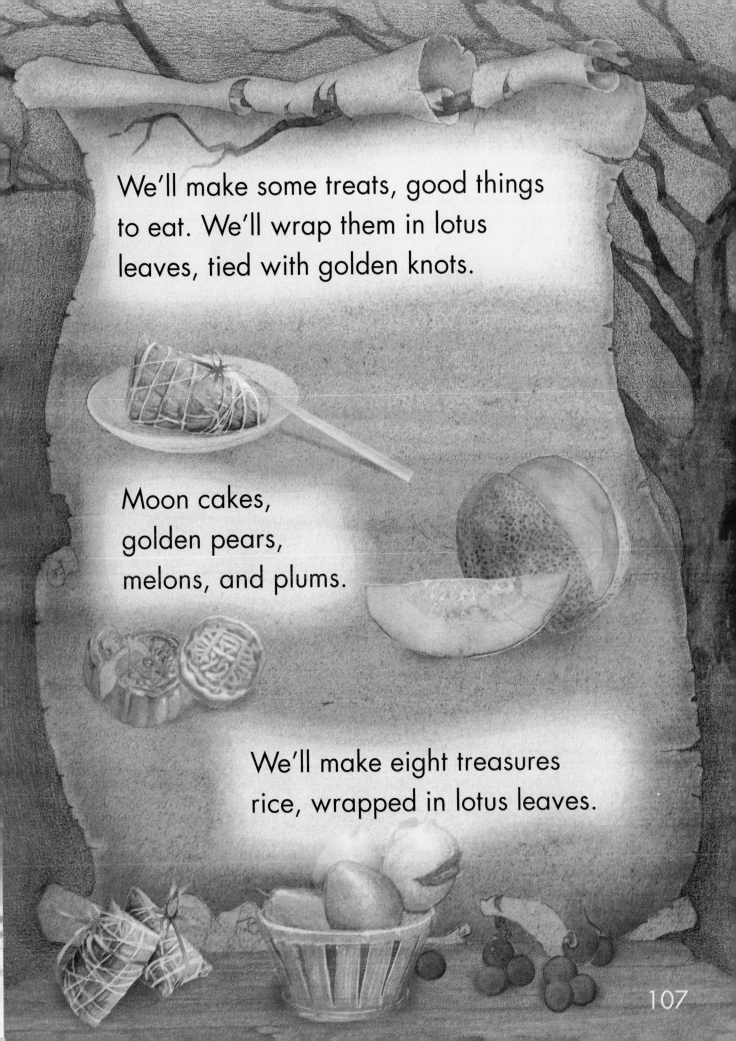

We'll make some treats, good things to eat. We'll wrap them in lotus leaves, tied with golden knots.

Moon cakes,
golden pears,
melons, and plums.

We'll make eight treasures rice, wrapped in lotus leaves.

Night is falling, and children call,

"Come out, Lady Moon. Come light up the sky."

High above the city, high above the hills, the moon shows her golden face. Children sing and laugh. They send their poems to the Lady in the Moon.

She glows, she glides, she grows.
Lady Moon fills the sky with light.
Let's laugh and sing a song to Lady Moon.
Let's read our poems to Lady Moon.

We'll make her some treats,
good things to eat. We'll
wrap them in lotus leaves,
tied with golden knots.

Moon cakes,
golden pears,
melons, plums, and
eight treasures rice.

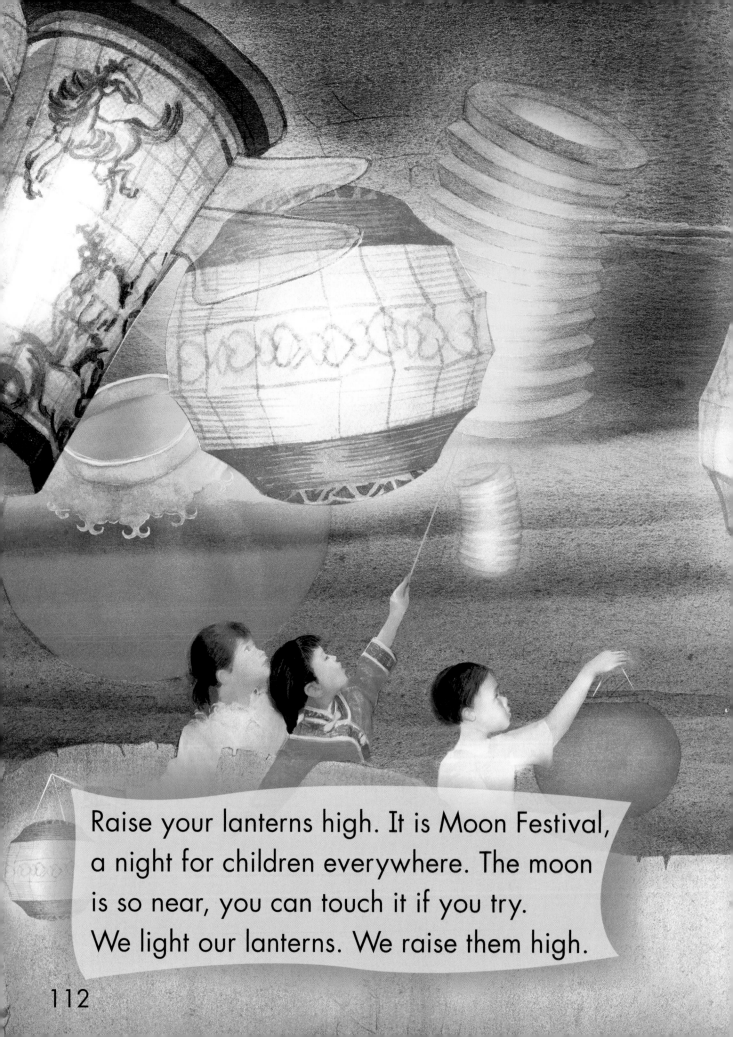

Raise your lanterns high. It is Moon Festival,
a night for children everywhere. The moon
is so near, you can touch it if you try.
We light our lanterns. We raise them high.

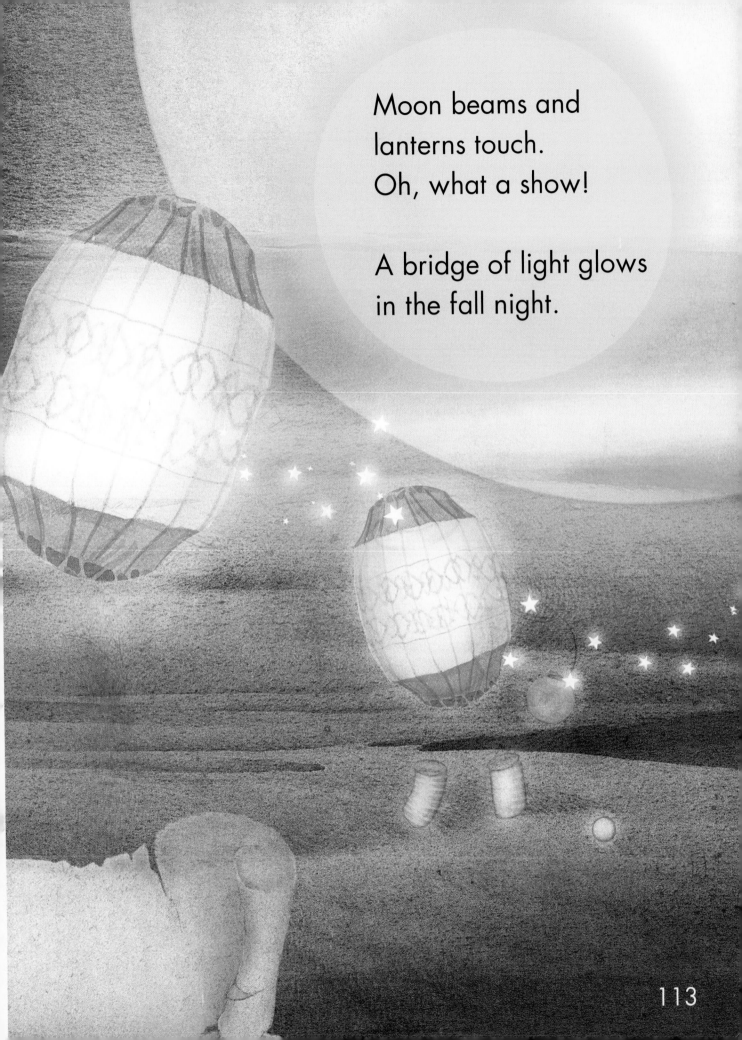

Moon beams and
lanterns touch.
Oh, what a show!

A bridge of light glows
in the fall night.

Where does it go?
Will it take us to the moon?

Let's laugh and sing a song to Lady Moon.
Let's read our poems to the Lady in the Moon.
We'll take her some treats, good things to eat.

We'll wrap them
in lotus leaves,
tied with golden knots.

Moon cakes,
golden pears,
melons, plums, and
eight treasures rice.

# Think and Share

**Talk About It** What part of the Moon Festival would be your favorite? Tell why.

**1.** Use the pictures below to retell important parts of *The Lady in the Moon.* **Retell**

**2.** Is this story realistic or a fantasy? Tell why. **Realism and Fantasy**

**3.** What did you wonder about as you read this story? What did you do to find out more? **Monitor/Fix Up**

**TEST PRACTICE** **Look Back and Write** When is the Moon Festival celebrated? Look back at page 113.

# Lily Wong Fillmore

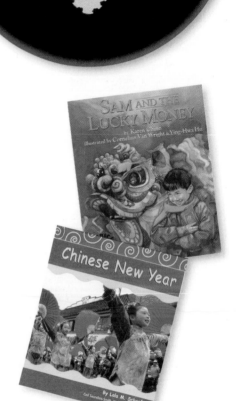

As a child, Lily Wong Fillmore loved the Moon Festival. It was a time to eat fruits and moon cakes. It was a time to stay up late and have fun.

"If clouds got near the moon, we children were told to make a lot of noise," says Ms. Fillmore. "No one wanted clouds to cover the moon. It was the one night of the year we could play outdoors and make as much noise as we pleased."

**Read more books about Asian celebrations.**

# My 4th of July

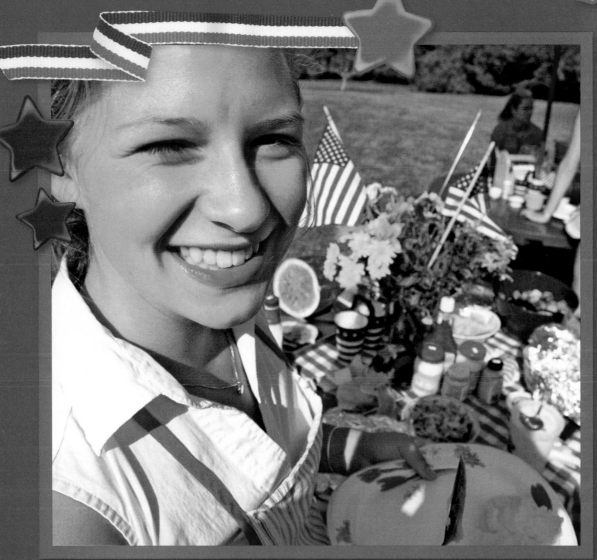

My family has fun on the 4th of July.
Mom bakes eight pies to share at the
block party.

We wrap red, white, and blue ribbons
on our bikes.

We laugh as we try to win the sack race.

Dad knows the best place to watch the fireworks at night. Crack! Bang! They light up the sky above us.

Will the fireworks touch the moon? We
laugh and cheer. What a beautiful sight!

## Poster

### Prompt

*The Lady in the Moon* describes special Moon Festival foods. Think about special foods your family eats on a holiday. Now write a poster that tells about these foods.

**Writing Trait**

Your **voice** shows how you feel about a topic.

**Student Model**

**Title tells what poster is about.**

**Writer tells about foods.**

**Last sentence shows writer's voice.**

Thanksgiving Dinner

Juicy turkey

Sweet pecan pie

Warm cranberry sauce

I love Thanksgiving.

# Grammar

## Adjectives for What Kind

An **adjective** can tell what kind.

**Happy** children picked **ripe** berries.

**Happy** tells what kind of children.
**Ripe** tells what kind of berries.

· · · · · · · · · · · · · · · · · · · · · · · · · · · · · ·

Look at the poster about Thanksgiving foods. Write the adjectives that tell what kind of turkey, what kind of pecan pie, and what kind of cranberry sauce.

# Let's Talk About
# Treasures to Share

# Words to Read

| stood |
| room |
| thought |
| picture |
| remember |

# Read the Words

Peter stood in his room. He thought he would take down his baby picture. Did anyone remember when he was a baby?

## Genre: Realistic Fiction

Realistic fiction has make-believe characters who act like real people. Next you will read about a boy who has a new baby sister.

# PETER'S CHAIR

## by Ezra Jack Keats

What is special
about Peter's chair?

Peter stretched as high as he could.
There! His tall building was finished.

CRASH! Down it came.

"Shhhh!" called his mother. "You'll have to play more quietly. Remember, we have a new baby in the house."

Peter looked into his sister Susie's room.
His mother was fussing around the cradle.

"That's my cradle," he thought, "and they
painted it pink!"

"Hi, Peter," said his father. "Would
you like to help paint Sister's high chair?"
"It's my high chair," whispered Peter.

He saw his crib and muttered, "My crib. It's painted pink too."

Not far away stood his old chair.

"They didn't paint that yet!" Peter shouted.

He picked it up and ran to his room.

"Let's run away, Willie," he said. Peter filled
a shopping bag with cookies and dog biscuits.

"We'll take my blue chair, my toy crocodile, and the picture of me when I was a baby."

Willie got his bone.

They went outside and stood in front of his house.

"This is a good place," said Peter. He arranged his things very nicely and decided to sit in his chair for a while.

But he couldn't fit in
the chair. He was too big!

His mother came to the window and called,
"Won't you come back to us, Peter dear? We
have something very special for lunch."

Peter and Willie made believe they didn't
hear. But Peter got an idea.

Soon his mother saw signs that Peter was home. "That rascal is hiding behind the curtain," she said happily.

She moved the curtain
away. But he wasn't there!

"Here I am," shouted Peter.

Peter sat in a grown-up chair.
His father sat next to him.

"Daddy," said Peter, "let's paint the little chair pink for Susie."

And they did.

149

# Think and Share

**Talk About It** Did you understand why Peter was sad? Have you ever felt as Peter did?

**1.** Use the pictures below to tell how Peter changed during the story. <sub>Retell</sub>

**2.** Who are the characters in the story? Where does the story take place?
Character/Setting

**3.** How does the story begin? How does it end? Story Structure

**Look Back and Write** Look back at pages 138–139. Make a list of what Peter and Willie take when they run away.

# Ezra Jack Keats

Ezra Jack Keats was an artist and author. He grew up in Brooklyn, New York, and often wrote about city life.

His first story about Peter, *The Snowy Day,* won the Caldecott Medal and made him famous. Mr. Keats died in 1983.

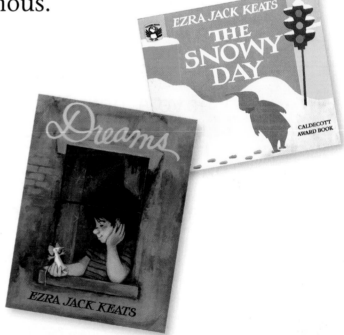

**Read more books by Ezra Jack Keats.**

# Peter's Baby Sister

Peter lives far from his grandmother. They share news by e-mail. See how.

| Write | Reply | Send | Forward | Delete | Address | Print |

Hi, Grandma!

I have a new little sister.
I thought of a great idea.
Remember my little blue chair?
I painted it and stood it in her bedroom.
Please come to see us.

Peter

Then Peter clicks his mouse on the SEND button. In a flash, Grandma gets Peter's e-mail. Grandma reads Peter's e-mail. Then she writes back.

Write    Reply    Send    Forward    Delete    Address    Print

Dear Peter,

I will visit next month.
I can't wait to see your new sister!
Would you send me a picture?

Grandma

Grandma is glad to hear from Peter. Peter is glad to hear from Grandma. They like to share news by e-mail.

# Write Now

## Writing and Grammar

### Facts

**Prompt**

*Peter's Chair* tells about Peter and his family.

Think about your family.

Now write facts about your family using number words.

**Writing Trait**

Follow **conventions** so readers can understand your facts.

**Student Model**

Each sentence tells a number fact.

Ideas are in order.

Writer uses <u>conventions</u> for sentences.

My family has five people.
Two people are grown-ups.
Three people are children.
They are two girls and one
boy. We also have four pets.

154

# Grammar

## Adjectives for How Many

Some **adjectives** tell how many.

Peter packed **five** cookies and **three** dog biscuits.

. . . . . . . . . . . . . . . . . . . . . . . . . . . . . .

Look at the family facts. Write the adjectives that tell how many.

# Let's Talk About
# Treasures to Share

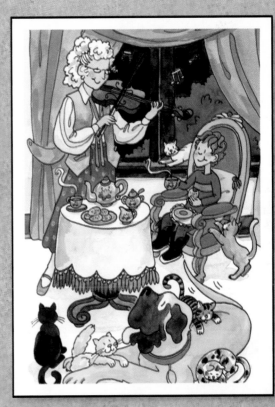

157

# Words to Read

told

only

across

because

dance

opened

shoes

# Read the Words

Henry told Mudge they were only going across the street to Mrs. Hopper's house. They were staying with Mrs. Hopper because Mom and Dad were going to a dance. Mrs. Hopper opened the door. Henry walked in and took off his shoes.

**Genre: Realistic Fiction**

Realistic fiction has settings that seem real, but the stories are made up. Next you will find out what happens when Henry and Mudge visit a neighbor.

# Henry and Mudge

and

## Mrs. Hopper's House

by Cynthia Rylant

illustrated by Carolyn Bracken
in the style of Suçie Stevenson

*What will Henry and Mudge
find at Mrs. Hopper's house?*

# A Sweetheart Dance

Valentine's Day was coming. Henry and his big dog Mudge loved Valentine's Day because of the candy. They liked the candy hearts that said "You're swell" and "Oh, dear" and things like that.

Henry read the words, and Mudge licked
them off. They were a good team.

On this Valentine's Day Henry's father and
Henry's mother were going to a Sweetheart
Dance. Henry and Mudge would be staying
with Mrs. Hopper.

Mrs. Hopper lived across the street in a big stone house with droopy trees and dark windows and a gargoyle on the door.

Henry liked Mrs. Hopper. But he did not like her house.

"Are you sure Mudge and I can't come to the Sweetheart Dance?" Henry asked his father.

"Only if you both promise to wear a
tuxedo and shiny black shoes and waltz to
'The Blue Danube,'" said Henry's father.

Henry looked at Mudge and tried to imagine him in a tuxedo and shiny black shoes, waltzing to "The Blue Danube."

"I think we'd better go to Mrs. Hopper's," Henry said.

"Good idea," said Henry's father.

"Because Mudge only knows how to tap-dance," Henry said with a grin.

# Costumes

Mrs. Hopper wasn't like anyone Henry had ever met. She played the violin for him. She served him tea. She told him about her father, who had been a famous actor.

She was very kind to Mudge. She cooked him a bowl of oatmeal and gave him his own loaf of French bread.

After the tea and music and oatmeal,
Mrs. Hopper took them upstairs. She
opened a room that had been her father's.

"Wow!" said Henry. The room was full
of costumes.

There were silk capes and tall hats and shiny coats. There were canes and swords and umbrellas. There were wigs.

Mrs. Hopper put a wig on Mudge.
"You look like a poodle, Mudge!"
said Henry.
Mudge wagged and wagged.

Henry and Mudge and Mrs. Hopper spent most of the evening in the costume room. They had a wonderful time.

And when Henry's parents came back from
the dance, were they ever surprised. Mudge
was a poodle, and Henry was a man! Henry
wore a tuxedo and a hat and shiny black shoes.

"I bet you didn't know I was this handsome," Henry told his dad. And everyone laughed and laughed.

# Think and Share

**Talk About It** Who do you think had a better time on Valentine's Day, Henry or his parents? Tell why you think as you do.

**1.** Use the pictures below to retell the story. **Retell**

**2.** How did Mrs. Hopper come to have so many costumes? **Cause/Effect**

**3.** How did the chapter titles help you as you read? **Preview**

**Look Back and Write** Look back at page 176. What does Henry say Mudge looks like? Why does Henry think that?

# Cynthia Rylant

Cynthia Rylant grew up in West Virginia. She says, "I lived in a place called Cool Ridge, in a four-room house with my grandparents. We had no running water and my grandparents grew and hunted most of our food."

Ms. Rylant has written many books about Henry and Mudge. Now she lives in Oregon with her dogs Martha Jane and Gracie Rose.

Read more Henry and Mudge books.

# Good Books, Good Times!

by Lee Bennett Hopkins
illustrated by Luciana Navarro Alves

Good books.
Good times.
Good stories.
Good rhymes.
Good beginnings.
Good ends.
Good people.
Good friends.
Good fiction.
Good facts.
Good adventures.
Good acts.
Good stories.
Good rhymes.
*Good* books.
*Good* times.

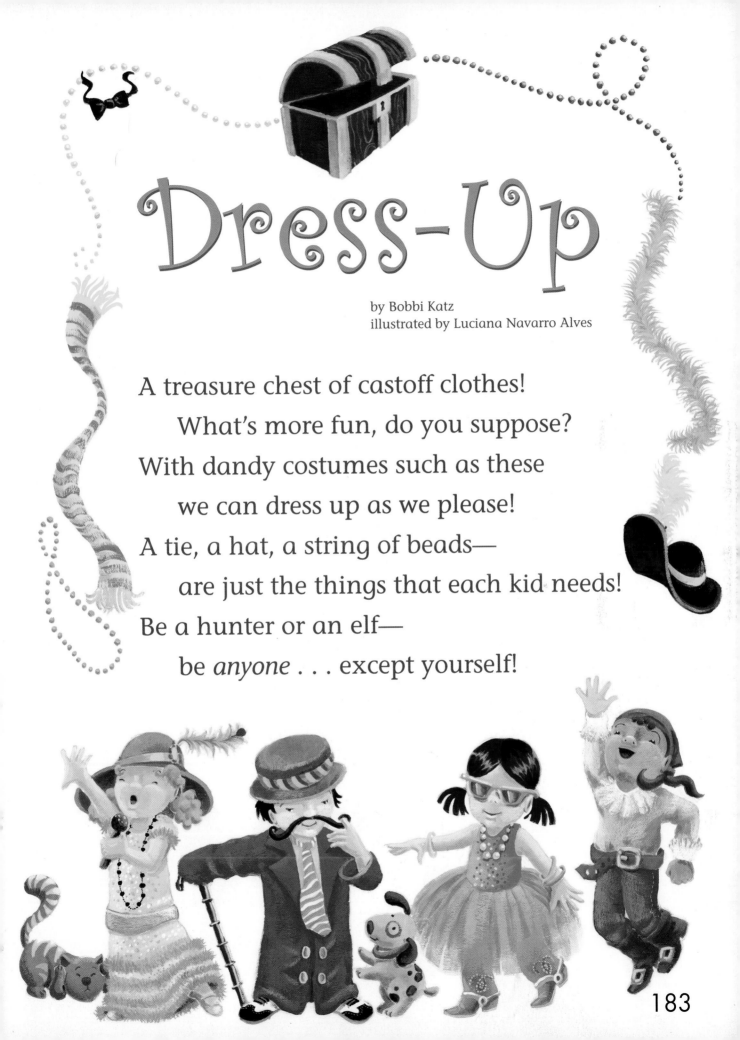

# Dress-Up

by Bobbi Katz
illustrated by Luciana Navarro Alves

A treasure chest of castoff clothes!
    What's more fun, do you suppose?
With dandy costumes such as these
    we can dress up as we please!
A tie, a hat, a string of beads—
    are just the things that each kid needs!
Be a hunter or an elf—
    be *anyone* . . . except yourself!

# Shell

by Myra Cohn Livingston
illustrated by Luciana Navarro Alves

When it was time
for Show and Tell,
Adam brought a big pink shell.

He told about
the ocean roar
and walking on the sandy shore.

And then he passed
the shell around.
We listened to the water sound.

And that's the first time
I could hear
the wild waves calling to my ear.

# Reading

by Marchette Chute
illustrated by Luciana Navarro Alves

A story is a special thing.
The ones that I have read,
They do not stay inside the book,
They stay inside my head.

# The Rainbow

by Iain Crichton Smith
illustrated by Luciana Navarro Alves

The rainbow's like a colored bridge
that sometimes shines from ridge to ridge.
Today one end is in the sea,
the other's in the field with me.

185

# Write Now

**Writing and Grammar**

## Explanation

**Prompt**

*Henry and Mudge* tells about Mrs. Hopper's special things. Think about something that is special to you. Now write an explanation telling why this thing is special.

**Writing Trait**

**Choose words** that tell what your special thing looks like.

**Student Model**

**First sentence tells main idea.** ——

**Writer tells why the quilt is special.**

My old red quilt is special. Grandma made it just for me. It has a chain of bright circles in the middle. It is warmer than a blanket. I use it on the coldest nights.

**Writer chooses vivid describing words.**

# Grammar

## Adjectives That Compare

Add **-er** to an adjective to compare two persons, places, animals, or things. Add **-est** to an adjective to compare three or more persons, places, animals, or things.

That dog is **faster** than Mudge.
Mudge is the **slowest** dog of all.

· · · · · · · · · · · · · · · · · · · · · · · · · · ·

Look at the explanation. Write the adjectives that compare.

## A Favorite Celebration

connect to
**WRITING**

Francisco learned from his mother that a celebration with family and friends is a treasure. What celebration is a treasure to you? Write about it.
Tell why you treasure this special time.

A Celebration I Treasure

One day my brother and I planned

188

## My Treasure

Think of one thing that is very special to you. Is it something you can see and touch? Is it a person or a pet? Tell a partner about it. Explain why it is a treasure to you.

## Something Old, Something New

People like Barnum Brown in *Mr. Bones* collect things that may seem odd to others. Get together with a partner. Talk about why old things may be as good as new things. Make a chart to show your ideas.

Treasures
Old Things | New Things

# Glossary

## Aa

**artist** An **artist** is a person who makes art. **Artists** can make pictures and statues.

artist

## Bb

bandanna

**bandannas** **Bandannas** are large, colored handkerchiefs.

**biscuits** **Biscuits** are small cakes that are not sweet.

**buñuelos** **Buñuelos** are sweet pastries that are fried and then covered with sugar. **Buñuelos** are like doughnuts, but smaller.

## Cc

**confetti** **Confetti** is bits of colored paper thrown about during celebrations. We threw **confetti** at the birthday party.

**cookies** **Cookies** are small, flat, sweet cakes.

cookies

**cowboy** A **cowboy** is a person who works on a cattle ranch. **Cowboys** also take part in rodeos.

cowboy

**cradle** A **cradle** is a small bed for a baby, usually one that can rock from side to side.

**crocodile** A **crocodile** is a large animal with thick skin, four short legs, and a pointed nose. **Crocodiles** look a lot like alligators.

crocodile

**curtain** A **curtain** is a cloth or other material hung across a window. **Curtains** are often used to keep out light.

**Ee**

**experimenting** When you are **experimenting,** you are testing or trying something out. The cook is **experimenting** with new recipes.

**Ff**

**festival** A **festival** is a special celebration. Some **festivals** include a parade.

festival

**Gg**

**gargoyle** A **gargoyle** is a decoration. It usually is made of stone and shaped like a scary animal or person. **Gargoyles** often decorate buildings.

gargoyle

**gigantic** Something that is **gigantic** is like a giant. Gigantic things are very large and strong. Some dinosaurs were **gigantic.**

**gold** **Gold** is a bright yellow metal that is worth a lot of money. **Gold** is used to make jewelry and some coins.

guitar

**guitar** A **guitar** is a musical instrument that usually has six strings. You play a **guitar** with your fingers.

## Hh

**heart** A **heart** is a figure shaped like this. ⟶ The card was covered with **hearts**.

heart

## Ii

**idea** An **idea** is a thought or plan. It was my **idea** to go to the zoo.

## Ll

**lizard** A **lizard** is a long, thin animal with dry, rough skin. **Lizards** look like very small crocodiles. Most **lizards** have four legs and a long tail.

lizard

**lotus leaves** **Leaves** are the flat, green parts of a tree or plant. A **lotus** is a water plant that has **leaves** and flowers.

## Mm

**Montana** **Montana** is one of the fifty states of the United States.

**museum** A **museum** is a building for keeping and showing interesting things. People visit art **museums,** science **museums,** and **museums** with things from long ago.

# Pp

**pears** **Pears** are sweet fruits that are round at one end. **Pears** are green or yellow and grow on trees.

pears

piñata

**piñata** A **piñata** is a decorated pottery pot filled with candy, fruit, and small toys. Blindfolded children swing sticks in order to break the **piñata** and get what is inside.

**poem** A **poem** is like a song without music. **Poems** often use words that rhyme. **Poems** sometimes put words together to tell about feelings and thoughts.

present

**present** A **present** is a gift. A **present** is something that someone gives you or that you give someone. His uncle sent him a birthday **present.**

196

# Ss

**shiny** Something that is **shiny** is bright. Mom gave me a **shiny** new penny.

**splash** If you **splash** water or some other liquid, you cause it to fly around.

splash

**squiggle** A **squiggle** is a wiggly twist or curve. The child drew a **squiggle** on the paper.

squiggle

**stared** If you **stared,** you looked at someone with your eyes wide open for a long time. I **stared** at my sister.

**straight** If something is **straight,** it does not have a bend, turn, or curve. She drew a **straight** line. Try to stand up **straight.**

197

# Tt

**tortilla** A **tortilla** is a thin, flat, round bread made of cornmeal. **Tortillas** are baked on a flat surface, filled with cheese or meat, and served hot.

**treasures** **Treasures** are things that are worth a lot. The pirates drew a map to show where the **treasures** were buried.

tuxedo

**tuxedo** A **tuxedo** is a formal suit for men. **Tuxedos** are usually black.

**tyrant** A **tyrant** is a mean, powerful ruler.

**Vv**   Valentine's Day **Valentine's Day** is February 14, a day when people send cards with hearts and small presents.

**Ww**   waltz To **waltz** means to dance slowly with graceful steps. Mom and Dad like to **waltz** together.

**waltz**

wonderful If something is **wonderful**, you like it very much. The ocean was a **wonderful** sight. She had a **wonderful** time at the party.

# Tested Words

## Mama's Birthday Present

about
enjoy
give
surprise
worry
would

## The Dot

colors
draw
drew
great
over
show
sign

## Mister Bones: Dinosaur Hunter

found
mouth
once
took
wild

## The Lady in the Moon

above
eight
laugh
moon
touch

# Tested Words

## Peter's Chair

picture
remember
room
stood
thought

## Henry and Mudge and Mrs. Hopper's House

across
because
dance
only
opened
shoes
told

# Acknowledgments

## Text

**Page 14:** "Mama's Birthday Present" by Carmen Tafolla, 1991. Reprinted by permission of Carmen Tafolla.

**Page 48:** *The Dot* by Peter H. Reynolds. Copyright © 2003 by Peter H. Reynolds. Reproduced by permission of the publisher Candlewick Press, Inc., Cambridge, MA.

**Page 76:** Reprinted with the permission of Aladdin Paperbacks, an imprint of Simon & Schuster Children's Publishing Division from *Mister Bones: Dinosaur Hunter* by Jane Kurtz, illustrated by Mary Haverfield. Text copyright © 2004 Jane Kurtz. Illustrations copyright © 2004 Mary Haverfield.

**Page 130:** *Peter's Chair* by Ezra Jack Keats, 1967. © Ezra Jack Keats Foundation. Reprinted by permission.

**Page 160:** Reprinted with the permission of Simon & Schuster Books for Young Readers, an imprint of Simon & Schuster Children's Publishing from *Henry and Mudge and Mrs. Hopper's House* by Cynthia Rylant, illustrated by Carolyn Bracken in the style of Suçie Stevenson. Text copyright © 2003 Cynthia Rylant. Illustrations, Copyrights © 2002 by Suçie Stevenson. All rights reserved.

**Page 182:** "Good Books, Good Times!" from *Good Rhymes, Good Times* by Lee Bennett Hopkins. Copyright © 1995 by Lee Bennett Hopkins. First appeared in *Good Rhymes, Good Times* published by HarperCollins Publishers. Reprinted by permission of Curtis Brown, Ltd.

**Page 183:** "Dress-Up" from *Poems for Small Friends* by Bobbi Katz, copyright © 1989 by Random House, Inc. Illustrations © 1989 by Gyo Fujikawa. Used by permission of Random House Children's Books, a division of Random House, Inc.

**Page 184:** "Shell" by Myra Cohn Livingston. Reprinted with the permission of Margaret K. McElderry Books, an imprint of Simon & Schuster Children's Publishing Division, from *World's I Know and Other Poems* by Myra Cohn Livingston. Text, Copyright © 1985 by Myra Cohn Livingston. All rights reserved.

**Page 185:** "Reading" from *Rhymes About Us* by Marchette Chute. Published by E.P. Dutton & Co., 1974. Reprinted by permission of Elizabeth Hauser.

**Page 185:** "The Rainbow" by Iain Crichton Smith from *A Scottish Poetry Book,* 1983. Reprinted by permission of Carcanet Press Limited.

## Illustrations

**Cover:** Daniel Moreton

**11-37, 42-43** Gabriel Pacheco

**99-117, 124-125** Lin Wang

**182-185** Luciana Navarro Alves

## Photographs

Every effort has been made to secure permission and provide appropriate credit for photographic material. The publisher deeply regrets any omission and pledges to correct errors called to its attention in subsequent editions.

Unless otherwise acknowledged, all photographs are the property of Scott Foresman, a division of Pearson Education.

Photo locators denoted as follows: Top (T), Center (C), Bottom (B), Left (L), Right (R), Background (Bkgd)

**4** (TL) ©Georgette Douwma/Getty Images, (CL) ©Gary W. Carter/Corbis

**8** (Bkgd) ©Dianna Sarto/Corbis, (TL) ©Georgette Douwma/Getty Images, (CL) ©Gary W. Carter/Corbis

**10** ©Stewart Cohen/Index Stock Imagery

**11** (BL) ©Jose Luis Pelaez, Inc./Corbis, (T) ©Royalty-Free/Corbis

**39** Courtesy of Carmen Tafolla

**69** Art Institute of Chicago, IL/Bridgeman Art Library

**72** (Bkgd) ©Louie Psihoyos/Corbis, (CL) ©Melissa Farlow/NGS Image Collection

**92** ©George White, Jr./Index Stock Imagery

**93** Field Museum of Natural History

**94** ©Discover Center

**95** (B) ©Andy Levin/Alamy Images, (T) ©Michael Prince/Corbis

**98** (Bkgd) Firefly Productions/Corbis, (R) ©Peter Steiner/Corbis

**99** (T) ©John Henley/Corbis, (CR) ©Dann Tardif/Corbis, (BR) ©Ariel Skelley/Corbis

**120** Creatas

**121** (T) ©Ariel Skelley/Corbis, (B) ©Paul Barton/Corbis

**122** ©Wayne Eastep/Getty Images

**126** ©Rob Lewine/Corbis

**151** ©The Ezra Jack Keats Foundation

**156** ©Brooklyn Productions/Getty Images

**157** (BL) Getty Images, (T) ©Patrick Molnar/Getty Images

**181** Photo of Cynthia Rylant used with permission of Simon & Schuster, Inc. ©Margaret Miller

**188** (CR) ©Comstock Inc., (BL) ©Georgette Douwma/Getty Images, (Bkgd) ©Dianna Sarto/Corbis

**189** (T) ©Jack Kurtz/The Image Works, Inc., (BR) ©Gary W. Carter/Corbis

**190** Hemera Technologies

**191** Hemera Technologies

**192** Hemera Technologies

**193** (TR) ©Nik Wheeler/Corbis, (BR) ©Paul Almasy/Corbis

**195** Getty Images

**196** (CL, BL, TR) Hemera Technologies

**197** ©Amwell/Getty Images

**198** ©Rubberball Productions/Getty Images

**199** ©Rob Lewine/Corbis

## Glossary

The contents of this glossary have been adapted from *First Dictionary.* Copyright © 2000, Pearson Education, Inc.

**READING STREET**